The Spur Book of

Chart and Compass

Rob Hunter

Frederick Warne

Published by
Frederick Warne (Publishers) Ltd
536 King's Road
London SW10 0UH

First published 1978
Reprinted (with revisions) 1983

Acknowledgement

The publishers would like to thank the Director and Staff of the National Sailing Centre, Cowes, Isle of Wight, for their help in the editing of this title.

ISBN 0 7232 3017 X

Printed and bound in Great Britain by
Galava Printing Company Ltd, Nelson, Lancs.

Contents

Introduction

About this Series

Venture Guides are written for that ever-growing host of people who enjoy outdoor leisure activities. They are written especially for the beginner, and fall into two broad categories.

The first concerns the skills that everyone who enjoys active leisure should possess, and covers such subjects as First Aid, Weather Lore, Knot Tying and Splicing, Survival and Rescue, and Map and Compass Skills, and Cooking and Camping.

The second covers Venture Sports, which are activities for the individual, and the individualist, and provides an introduction to such sports as Hill Trekking, Backpacking, Rock Climbing, Sailing, Snorkelling, Downhill and Cross Country Ski-ing, and Small Boat Handling.

This book, *Chart and Compass*, is designed as an introduction to Offshore Navigation for small boat or dinghy sailors.

About this Book

This is a book for absolute beginners. It is written in the simplest terms to give a basic grasp of the subject.

There is far more in this book about the compass than there is about charts. It is likely that anyone venturing to sea will have some familiarity with land maps, and there is only one major difference with a chart. Given a land map that shows a church, at least when you get there you can see the church. Most of the features on a sea chart you will never see, because they are submerged all the time. You may well detect their presence by other means, which we will come to later. But you cannot see them.

There must be very few places in Britain where you can walk for more than two or three miles in a straight line without seeing some recognisable feature to check your course and position. Even a change in gradient from uphill to downhill, or crossing a small brook will give you a clue of some kind. At sea, two or three miles is virtually nothing, and anyone who can use a chart and compass at all will soon be crossing estuaries or bays ten miles wide without any trouble, except the boat keeps jumping!

This book is designed to explain the basics of buying and installing compasses; reading charts; plotting courses and preparing for and monitoring your passage on a short small-boat cruise. Advice on further training is also given.

Most of you will have bought this book because you have a small boat, and to use it properly you will need to have some knowledge of simple navigation.

'Simple' navigation (if there is such a thing) when concerned with estuary or coastal cruising is more often called pilotage. You need to have an understanding of the following:

1. Compasses.
2. Charts.
3. Tides.
4. Buoyage.
5. Course-plotting.
6. Fixes.

This list could be extended, but if you know all this simply and well, you will have made a good start, and this book will therefore concentrate on these subjects. Other titles in this series, notably *Weather Lore*, will give useful background information.

1
Selecting and Installing a Compass

A compass and, let me stress, an accurate compass has far more importance at sea than on land. Every boat venturing offshore for more than a few yards should carry one, if only as a safety measure. Fog can descend quickly, visibility is restricted from the cockpit of a dinghy, and even a short cruise can become dangerous if you don't know where you are. The great rule, let me state it at once, is

ALWAYS KNOW WHERE YOU ARE

Compasses: There are many kinds of compass, so let us be clear that we refer here to a MARINE, magnetic compass. All magnetic compasses rely on the fact that a long and narrow piece of magnetized metal will, if properly balanced, point NORTH. Beyond that vast simplification lies a world of differences between the compass costing £1 and the one costing several hundred pounds.

You will need to have two considerations in mind. Firstly, and most important, the degree of accuracy required, and secondly, what you can afford to pay.

Popular compasses range upwards in price from £25 to £150. Buy the best you can afford. If you avoid pretty packaging and gadgets, you will, by and large, get what you pay for.

Steering Compasses

For the dinghy or small boat, the main compass will be fixed inboard, and is called a 'steering compass'. Your first consideration is to check that you can read the 'compass card' easily. The 'compass card' is the swivelling card or disc within the compass bowl, marked in degrees and/or with the 'points' of the compass NORTH (N), WEST (W), S.E., N.E. and so on. The 360° rotation is now almost universal, and although you will not need, and may not be able, to steer within 5° of a given point, you must check the readability of the card (and your own eyesight).

Some compasses have a magnifying lens over the 'card'. The course is read off at a point or line on the dial called the 'lubber line', and if this area is magnified it is easier to see.

There are, broadly speaking, two sorts of steering compass, the flat grid steering type, and the graduated card type, which can

9

FIGURE 1

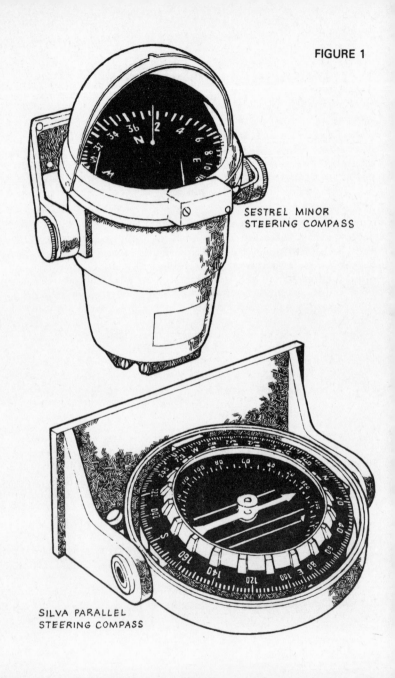

SESTREL MINOR
STEERING COMPASS

SILVA PARALLEL
STEERING COMPASS

perhaps be mounted at eye level. Popular makes are RITCHIE, SESTREL, SUUNTO or SILVA. (Fig. 1).

Finally, before buying a compass, consider your own boat. There are various ways of mounting a compass, and it is largely a matter of convenience. If, for example, you intend mounting it on a bulkhead, be sure the compass has the appropriate fittings to enable vou to do so.

Hand-Bearing Compasses (Fig. 2).

A hand-bearing compass, if you can afford it, is a very useful addition, and can double up as a steering compass in an emergency. They are very useful equipment in small boats, and you will find them useful for taking bearings on the shore, or measuring angles on approaching ships.

Adjusters

Any compass worth buying will have some device for adjusting the compass to compensate for 'deviation' (of which more later), which is caused by metal or electrical fittings in the boat. Find out where the 'adjusters' are, how they work, and be sure they will be accessible when the compass is installed. This applies to fixed mounted compasses, not to the hand-bearing type.

Pivot Stiffness

All compass pivots have some stiffness. Check that the pivot is not *too* stiff by placing the compass on some flat surface, noting the bearing, and then gently move the compass off that bearing, let it settle, then move it, gently, back again to exactly the same first position. The compass needle should swing freely and return to the same bearing. If there is too much stiffness in the pivot there will be a difference, and if this is over about 5°, the compass is not suitable for any sort of coastal work.

Points on Buying

Don't buy in a hurry. Buy a reputable make. Do buy from a ship chandler or compass manufacturer. They are not cheap, but get a good one. Check for bubbles or damage. And remember, buying is only the first step.

Installing the Compass

You must appreciate that, to be effective in use, your compass must be correctly installed.

You may feel that, having carried your expensive new toy back on board, and wedged it in place in some handy spot, you can then embark on a 20 mile cruise. If so, you are in for a nasty

11

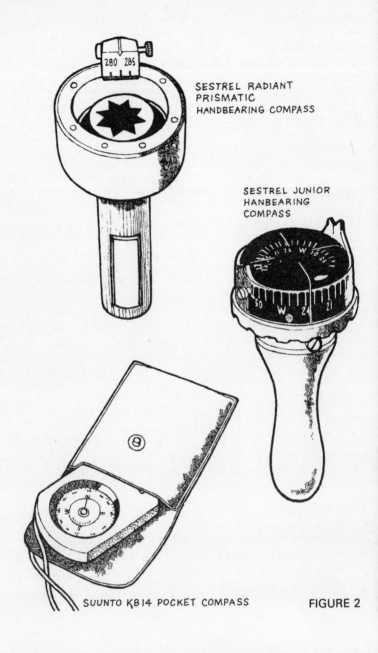

SESTREL RADIANT
PRISMATIC
HANDBEARING COMPASS

SESTREL JUNIOR
HANBEARING
COMPASS

SUUNTO KB14 POCKET COMPASS

FIGURE 2

surprise. No compass is any use until *proved, checked* and *adjusted*.

Compass Fittings

Most steering compasses will be fitted with 'gimbals' which enable the compass to remain level as the boat heels or rolls. Others rely on the compass card floating in a sphere.

Be sure that your compass remains accurate and readable whatever the position of the craft.

Choosing the Position

The first and most important point is to place the compass where you can see and read it easily—and comfortably—from the steering position. Don't neglect the comfort—you may need to keep staring at the compass for hours, and if this means twisting your neck round you will end up very tired indeed.

It is most important to look straight at the compass, either directly down on the horizontal type, or to look directly in line with the boat with a vertical type. (Fig. 3).

Interference

The principal thing to avoid during installation is metallic or electric interference, causing 'deviation' or distorting of the compass reading. It is all but impossible to eliminate deviation, but it is possible to reduce it.

The biggest cause of interference is the engine, inboard or outboard; then dynamos, batteries, radios, logs, echo sounders, wiring, metal objects, anchors, shrouds. Study your chosen compass position for all these, and keep away from them.

On a wood or GRP craft the difficulties lessen to a reasonable proportion if you can maintain clearance of *3 feet or more* from the worst offenders. (Fig. 4).

Stowage

You may decide to install your compass while on the beach or at anchor. It's a nice job for an afternoon in early spring. Then comes your first cruise, and you load on board your spare anchor, a radio set, a sack of tinned goodies, and assorted tools—bang goes your deviation calculations, and on go more sources of interference. You must have regular places for stowage, and check your compass (see over) when the boat is, in all respects, ready for sea.

However, before we start adjusting the compass, but bearing these points in mind, let us get on with the installation.

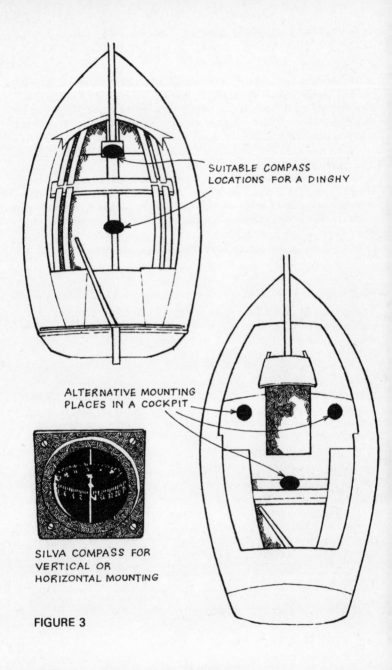

SUITABLE COMPASS
LOCATIONS FOR A DINGHY

ALTERNATIVE MOUNTING
PLACES IN A COCKPIT

SILVA COMPASS FOR
VERTICAL OR
HORIZONTAL MOUNTING

FIGURE 3

Lining up the Compass

A very common source of serious error comes when lining up the compass with the boat.

The boat must point correctly down the desired compass course, and unless the compass is lined up exactly on or parallel to the fore—and—aft line of the boat, the compass will point in one direction, and you will be heading in another.

DO NOT assume that bulkheads, thwarts, lockers, etc., are either parallel or square to the keel—get out a spirit level and set-up some marks.

Should you detect an error, do not be surprised. Check your measurements carefully, and if convinced of an error set up wooden blocks or wedges, sloped in the required direction, and screwed firmly into place to hold the compass. This is better than loose packing, as you can remove the compass for safe keeping without losing the correct adjustment.

Check and *check* again, and have someone else *check*, when you have finally lined up your compass, that all is in order.

Beware of magnetic attraction

FIGURE 4

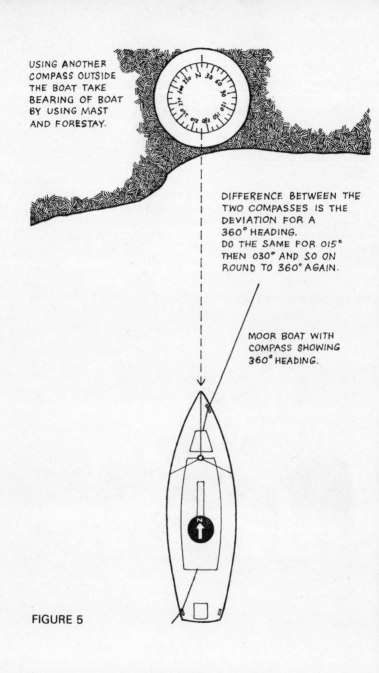

USING ANOTHER COMPASS OUTSIDE THE BOAT TAKE BEARING OF BOAT BY USING MAST AND FORESTAY.

DIFFERENCE BETWEEN THE TWO COMPASSES IS THE DEVIATION FOR A 360° HEADING.
DO THE SAME FOR 015° THEN 030° AND SO ON ROUND TO 360° AGAIN.

MOOR BOAT WITH COMPASS SHOWING 360° HEADING.

FIGURE 5

2
Adjusting the Compass

Once the compass is installed, it must be adjusted, to minimise deviation. Let us be clear exactly what 'deviation' is.

Deviation

All compasses contain errors, and they add up to what is described as the *TOTAL COMPASS ERROR*. Deviation is part of the compass error, and can be caused by many things: interference, incorrect installation, electrical storms, or magnetic attraction, to name but a few. Two points about deviation are crucial . . .

1. Deviation will vary with every boat.
2. Deviation will vary with every compass heading.

You have, therefore, to know the deviation for your craft on various compass headings, and the best way to do this is to prepare a deviation card (see over).

Detecting the Errors

Before there is any question of adjustment, you must be able to detect the errors, and for this you will require a fixed, known and reliable reference point. Provided it has these three qualities, almost any reference point will do. Between your craft, and the *known* magnetic bearing of this reference point, and the *actual* bearing of the reference bearing *shown on your compass*, lies a difference, and this is the deviation.

Remember that (point 2 above) the deviation will vary on different headings. So it is necessary to swing the boat round and check out the deviation on different headings.

The steps most commonly employed are as follows:

1. Load the boat and stow as usual.
2. Moor the boat fore and aft, lined up on some fixed reference point — a church spire — lighthouse. Write down the magnetic bearing — calculated off map or chart, then check with the bearing given by your compass.
3. Swing the boat round gradually through the 16 points of the compass (see p. 9) and note down the deviation at each point.
4. Write down these deviations on your Deviation Card. Fig. 5 shows another method and either will be suitable for a small boat.

17

It may well be possible to damp out some of the more extreme variations by using the compass adjusters, which are small screw adjusters fitted to most marine compasses.

Compass Adjusting: Compass Adjusters

Read the instructions carefully, and correct half way into the error. If on North it gives an error of $+6°$ adjust out $3°$. Then check on the exact opposite heading, i.e. South, and again adjust half of the error. In this way you may gradually reduce it to acceptable size.

You may be able to get help from an experienced friend, but if the deviations are very large you must get an expert and you may well need to send for a professional compass adjuster. Any harbour master will be able to put you in touch with one, and although their services are not cheap, if you have spent £100 on a compass and hours installing it correctly in your precious craft, it makes sense to ensure that it gives you accurate and reliable information.

Deviation Cards

Provided you are not always moving the anchors or radios about, the deviation will probably remain constant on any particular heading. So, if you record the heading (or course) you will be able to use the information to correct the compass reading on that course heading at some future date. Remember that deviation related to the *boat* and course, and wherever you are, in the Channel or Pacific, it will be the same.

You then collect this information together on a Deviation Card, giving the compass heading, and the adjustment necessary to correct it. You can give this either as a plus (+) or minus (-) or by an East (E) or West (W). For example, if your desired heading was North (360°M) but your compass reads 357°M you would need to add 3°M to get the right heading. So Magnetic Heading 0° but deviation $+3°$ (3E) Compass Heading 003°M. If you set 003° on the compass you have allowed for deviation and are heading due North.

COURSE	DEVIATION
N	2°E
NE	3°E
E	5°W
SE	2°W
S	2°W
SW	4°E
W	3°E
NW	4°E

or like this

    Course = 167°M
    Deviation = 3°E
    Compass Course = 164°C

Final Check

Once you have checked (or swung) your compass through the 16 points, there is one simple, but useful, check to make certain that you have not put in a plus instead of a minus, or added in the date!

Simply add or subtract all the corrections and divide by the number of corrections (in this case 16). The average correction ought to be zero, but it is unlikely to be so unless you are very lucky or have been meticulous. In any event, the error should not be more than 1°, and if it is, then the compass needs rotating slightly, or the fore and aft alignment needs checking.

Before we go on to Charts, let us just summarise what we have covered in these first chapters.

1. Buy the best compass you can afford from a reputable stockist.
2. Consider where and how you will install it.
3. Align the lubber line on the compass with the fore and aft line on the boat. Watch out for causes of deviation.
4. Check the compass on 16 points, against some fixed reference point and see Fig 5 for alternative method.
5. Prepare a deviation card.
6. Check the calculations on your deviation card.

Now notice that check, check and check again is the watchword. If in any doubt, get expert help from an experienced friend, or get professional advice. Now let's look at charts.

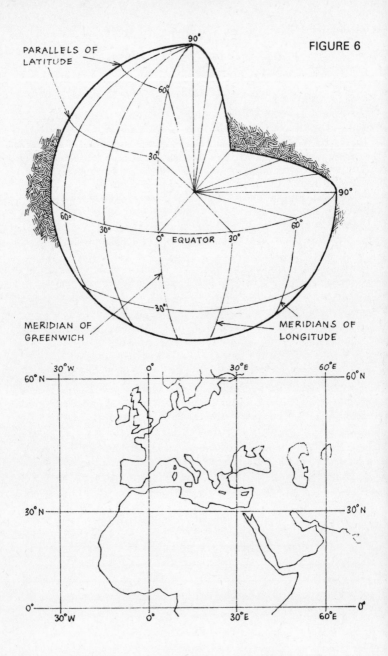

FIGURE 6

PARALLELS OF LATITUDE

90°

60°

30°

90°

60° 30° 0° EQUATOR 30° 60°

90°

30°

MERIDIAN OF GREENWICH

MERIDIANS OF LONGITUDE

60°N 30°W 0° 30°E 60°E 60°N

30°N 30°N

0° 0°
30°W 0° 30°E 60°E

3
Charts and Pilotage Publications

The first thing you will learn about charts is the cost! It may horrify you, but there is nothing you can do about it except look after them carefully. You will need an Admiralty chart to follow this chapter.

Choice
The most complete range of charts is produced by the Admiralty. There are two other chartmakers, Stanfords and Imrays. These two are good and produce charts to the more popular cruising areas. The references in this book are to Admiralty charts, but whichever make you choose, stick to it. In that way you become familiar with them, and they become easy to read. Note the publication date and always buy the most recent one.

What is a Chart?
A chart is a scale-illustration of the seabed and coastline, drawn to various scales and indicating by colours, marks and symbols such information as depth, channels, buoys and lights. They have a great deal in common with the land based OS maps and if you are already familiar with OS maps, you will have made a good start towards understanding charts. *The Spur Book of Map and Compass* will teach you about the OS maps and, for dinghy cruising, OS maps are invaluable.

Reading a Chart: CHART 5011
The Admiralty have produced a book, although, being the Admiralty, they *call* it a chart, Number 5011. It is available from all good chandlers and chart agents, and with it you will be able to interpret all the signs, colours and symbols on the chart.

Buy a 5011 and spend an evening or two browsing over it. It will give you all the information you need on the charts themselves, and here we will only cover the relevance of certain features to course plotting.

Latitude and Longitude
The lines that run vertically down the chart are lines of *longitude*. The lines that run horizontally across the chart are lines of *latitude*. (Fig. 6).

21

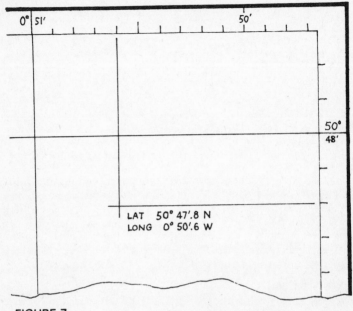

FIGURE 7

Latitude expresses the angular distance North or South of the Equator in degrees. Each degree is subdivided in 60 Minutes, and each minute into sixty seconds, which won't effect us much.

Minutes of Latitude are useful for: 1 minute of latitude = 1 nautical mile. You can, therefore, use the latitude scale on the side of the chart as your distance scale. (Fig. 7).

It is worth noting here that whenever you take the distance measurement off the latitude scale, you do so at a point as near as possible parallel to your position on the chart. You don't go to the top of the scale if your plotted course runs along the bottom of the chart.

Compass Rose
One feature not found on a map is the compass rose. There will be several of these compass rings on the chart, each consisting of two circles. The outer ring shows true NORTH, and the inner ring gives magnetic north. (Fig. 8).

FIGURE 8

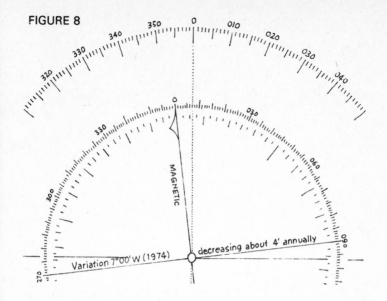

True and Magnetic Bearings: Variation

Within the compass rose the variation (from True to Magnetic) is noted, and the annual rate of change.

Variation must not be confused with Deviation. Variation is the angular difference between True North (the direction of the North Pole) and Magnetic North. The Magnetic Pole is situated somewhere to the North of Canada and to this pole all compass needles point. The Magnetic Pole is not fixed, but moves a little each year. This annual change can be calculated, and is shown on the 'compass rose' of the charts.

The variation differs according to where you are due to the varying effect of the magnetic pole. All good sailors work from and to the True bearing, but, thanks to the inner (magnetic) ring on the compass rose, it is possible to do most of your calculations on magnetic, and in small boats stay in magnetic O.

Remember, the variation varies, and using an old chart, the actual magnetic bearing may not be accurate if you fail to take variation into account. Moreover, much of the supporting navigational advice is in True, and has to be converted.

On the other hand, working in magnetic is quicker, and with fewer calculations there is less risk of error.

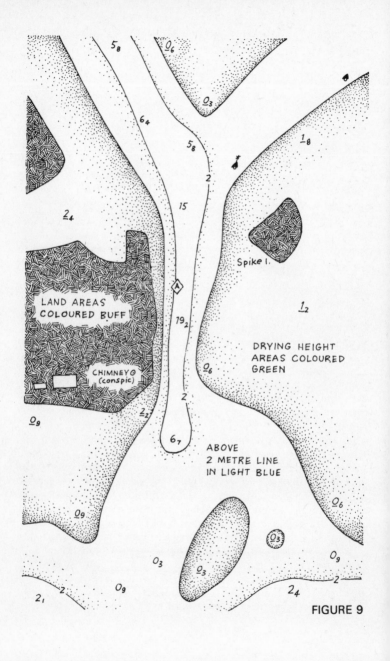

FIGURE 9

However, let it be understood that for beginners we are working from *True* bearings.

Variation and Deviation

Two vessels *in the same spot* would, because of their different loads and fittings, have different *deviations* but the same variation. The same vessel in two different spots, would have the same deviation, but different variation.

A vessel in the Channel would have one variation, but if she then sailed in the Mediterranean, would have a different one, while the deviation would stay the same. Got it?

Scale

The best scale for use on small craft is 1:75000, which makes 1" = 1 nautical mile (approx.) A nautical mile is about 6,080 feet. Another popular scale with estuary or dinghy sailors is 1:20,000 which gives lots of detail. Note that a knot = a sea mile *per hour*. It is a measurement of time as well as distance.

Chart Catalogue

A useful Admiralty publication is the *Catalogue of Admiralty Charts and Hydrographic Publications*. This tells you which are the newest charts, and gives a list of chart agents. Any chart bought from their agents will have been corrected up to the moment of sale. In 1982 the cost of the UK edition was £1.50 and of the worldwide edition £8.90.

Chart Corrections

If you are familiar with OS maps you will know that housing estates or timber felling can alter the landscape yet go unrecorded for years on the map. Much the same is true of charts. Buoyage in the main shipping lanes does not change much, but inshore sandbanks do shift, harbour works are built and there are wrecks and prohibitions.

Notices to Mariners

Your charts can be corrected by reading the Admiralty-issued 'Notices to Mariners' which are issued frequently and available to any interested party. As they cover the whole world, finding the bit that affects you can be tedious so you can refer to extracts in the yachting press or, before the summer cruise, send your relevant charts to a chart agent who will update them for a small fee—or sell you new charts if yours have gone out of date and beyond reasonable recall!

Converting True to Magnetic and Back

To convert a True bearing to a magnetic one, you *add* Westerly variations and *subtract* easterly ones.

To convert magnetic (compass) bearings to True, you *subtract* Westerly ones, and *add* Easterly ones.

Metric Charts (Fig. 9).

In recent years, most Admiralty charts have gone metric. This will not affect scale or distance, as everyone, even the French, has stuck to the existing system using *MILLES* for Miles and *NOUEDS* for speed. It does, however, affect DEPTH, which is now measured in metres (39") instead of the old fathoms. Buoyage, which we shall cover later is also being changed.

One final thought. Even though non-Admiralty charts don't get the same attention with regard to corrections, they go out of date just as fast. Earlier we stressed the care necessary with installing and checking the compass. The same meticulous attention is necessary with charts. The result of this attention, if extended to course-plotting and weather lore as well, will be a happy and safe cruise.

Drying Heights and Soundings

One helpful point: you will find the chart covered with little figures like $\underline{2}$ and 6_7.

The first example indicates a drying height, i.e., an area which is above chart-datum and the figures tell you that this is a spot which stands 2 metres above chart datum at low tide.

All the 'soundings', like our second example, 6_7, are depths below chart datum, and, in simple terms, even at low water you will be in 6.7 metres of water. So unless your boat draws 6.8 metres you have no problem.

4

Navigation Instruments and Books

Though the compass is the main instrument, and the chart the main source of information, various other bits and pieces are necessary, or desirable, in various degrees. (Fig. 10).

To calculate causes and transfer them from chart to compass you need, apart from a good compass (or two), and charts, the following aids or information.

1. Tidal flow charts, or tidal stream atlases.
2. Dividers.
3. Parallel Rule and/or Douglas Protractor.
4. Several B or 2B pencils.
5. A soft rubber.
6. A reliable watch.
7. A good pair of binoculars.

Keep the charts in a plastic sleeve, and stow the other items somewhere secure where they can't roll under the floorboards.

Reeds Nautical Almanac

This annual publication is the Bible of the cruising fraternity. It's not cheap—£9.95—but you can hardly do without it.

Tide Tables

Tide tables are a 'must', and the more comprehensive the better. If you buy a Reeds Almanac, to help with compass adjusting, you will also find that it contains very good Tide Tables. Beware of relying too much on so-called 'constants', related to a port a very long way away, because the time differences are anything but constant. There are constants for all sorts of ports around the entire coast of the British Isles, and you must choose the nearest one.

Tide Flow Charts: Tidal Stream Atlases

Tidal currents do not always run in agreement with High and Low Water. In the southern entrance to the Irish Sea, for example, at H.W. the currents are almost at their maximum. Please accept that it is absolutely necessary to use good LOCAL tables, for both height of tides and currents, and direction, and get good local

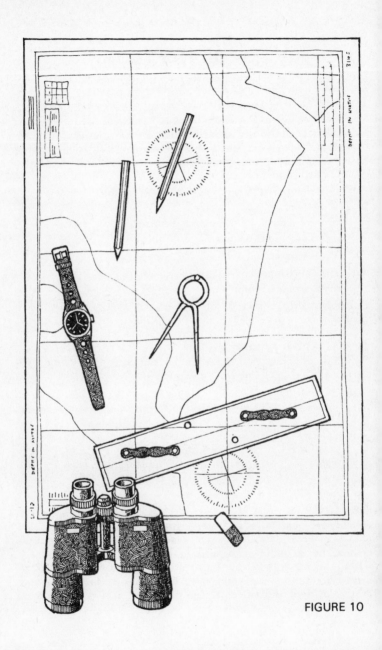

FIGURE 10

advice from coastguard or fisherman, on the tides on your part of the coast.

'Reeds' show many tidal currents, and there are Admiralty Tidal Atlases for various places, and many Admiralty charts carry further detailed information, as also do Admiralty Pilots. Use whichever gives the greatest detail for the area with which you are immediately concerned, and ask advice as well. Stanfords charts have tidal flow arrows on them.

Pencils, Rulers, Dividers, Parallel Rule

The actual instruments consist basically of several soft pencils — already sharpened — a soft rubber, a pair of dividers, and a parallel rule. The dividers are for measuring distance against the scale of latitude on the side of the chart, and the parallel rule is for transferring bearings to the nearest compass rose. An old-fashioned round office rule will serve for parallels, and at one time I used a piece of ⅜" brass rod to roll across the chart. As this also served to hold the kettle on the stove it was doubly useful. You can do the job with a normal rule and set-square, but it does seem to need three hands.

There are more exotic instruments of many kinds, but the list given here will serve for a start. As with many other things though, when buying such items, buy good ones. Even with pencils, those from a drawing office supplier are really vastly superior to the ones bought from a toy shop. I prefer grade B, though some people prefer 2B. Never use hard pencils on a chart, because the marks do not rub off.

Chart Tables

One is apt to say lightheartedly 'on the chart table you will need ...' The problem in most small boats is to find space for a chart table. It may have to be a piece of plywood balanced on your knees, though it really is worth having a fixture if you possibly can. If at all possible, make it about 3' x 2' which will allow a chart with only a single fold, plus a little bit of space for pencils, dividers, etc. You may have to accept more folding, but however you achieve it, some kind of flat, rigid surface is almost essential. It is worth incorporating clips, pockets, trays, or some sort of holding device for the chart instruments, since the movement of a boat will certainly send them flying about everywhere. Have some big clips and rubber bands or shock cord clipped on to stow things under. Cover it with a plastic sheet to keep the spray off.

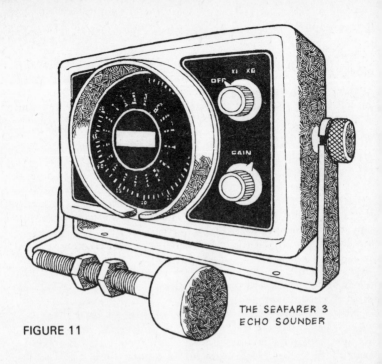

THE SEAFARER 3
ECHO SOUNDER

FIGURE 11

Echo Sounders (Fig. 11).

You must have some means of measuring depth of water. The old-fashioned way was by means of a weight, usually of lead, on a long line. It required considerable skill to use in a moving boat, and brought about the phrase *'Swinging the Lead'* to mean dodging work. It is true that it did save the olden time sailor from the much harder physical labour of mast climbing, sail furling and so on, but if you try 'sounding' with a lead line you will soon discover that it is far from easy. The line ties itself round everything in sight, including your own feet!

Since echo sounders are now small, cheap and almost completely reliable, they have become the standard in small yachts, but are still rare in dinghies, where the centreboard coming up is usually the first sign of a shoal. There are many available at around £60 to £80, and given only reasonable common-sense they are easy to install and use. As a navigational instrument, an echo sounder is second only to a compass. Buying one today you should make sure that it reads in metres, even though it may well

30

have fathoms and feet as well. **ALL NEW** charts have depths in metres, and the echo sounder is better if it agrees directly with the chart without the need to convert the readings. The depth under the boat is often a good guide to your position.

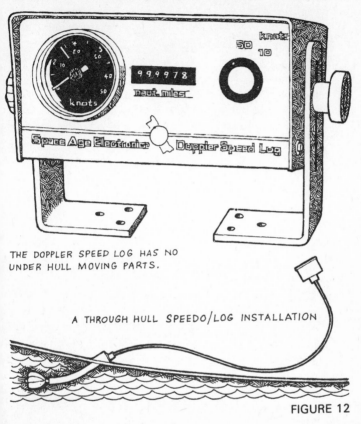

THE DOPPLER SPEED LOG HAS NO UNDER HULL MOVING PARTS.

A THROUGH HULL SPEEDO/LOG INSTALLATION

FIGURE 12

Logs (Fig. 12).

Some means of measuring distance is needed, though it is possible to use time and speed multiplied together if you know your own boat well. The instrument is called a 'log'. The old-fashioned, and still very reliable ones use a long trailing rope with an impeller towed well behind the boat to a shaft of a type of meter. Nowadays, most people have various kinds of electronic

31

logs, which show speed as well as distance. They can be good, but most need considerable care in setting up and calibrating, and those relying on small impellers are rather prone to fouling weed. The most reliable small log in my experience is a purely mechanical one called a SUMLOG, driven by a flexible cable, like a car speedometer, though electronic models are rapidly improving.

Dutchman's Log

The dinghy sailor is not likely to have a log trailing behind, but if he knows the length of his craft he can make an accurate calculation either by timing the boat past a floating object—like a beer can, or having the crew throw some object (not plastic) overboard. The helmsman can see it hit the water and time it past the boat. This is commonly referred to as the Dutchman's Log.

5
Tides

The small boat sailor must understand and use the tides. They can be a great asset, or a complete hindrance, and even a danger.

The study of how the tides arrive at various places is most interesting, and very complex.

There is no space here to do more than explain that tides arrive from the Atlantic and are divided and diverted up the English Channel, Bristol Channel and Irish Sea. Sometimes they meet, as at Liverpool, where the tide running up the Irish Sea meets that coming round the North of Ireland, and this leads, of course, to very large tides at Liverpool. In other places, the High Tide from one direction meets the Low Tide from another direction, and they cancel each other out. Rivers, estuaries and freshwater flows lead to further complications.

Springs and Neaps

A tide table will show you that tidal phases change daily. A tide takes about six hours to come in or 'flood', then there is a brief pause (slack water) before it starts to go out (ebb). The ebb also usually takes six hours.

Affected by the moon, the height of the tide also varies, and is divided into SPRINGS, which is a tide with the HIGHEST HIGH WATER and LOWEST LOW WATER: and NEAPS, which are the LOWEST HIGH WATER and the HIGHEST LOW WATER. The difference is called the tidal 'range' and as you can see, the range is much wider at 'Springs' than at 'Neaps'. If you ran aground hard at HIGH WATER SPRINGS, you might have to wait until the next H.W.S. to get you off again.

Chart Datum

Most charts give depths calculated to a chart datum, a water level of the lowest tide that can conceivably occur. This is called the L.A.T. (Lowest Astronomical Tide) and it supposes that, at the worst, there would always be that much water at that particular point.

Some charts, however, give a chart datum based on *Mean Low Water Springs* (M.L.W.S.) which is only an average of low tides at that spot and in this case, it is conceivable (although unlikely) that sometimes the water depth there will be less than that shown on the chart.

FIGURE 13

HOW THE FLOOD TIDE ADVANCES AROUND BRITAIN

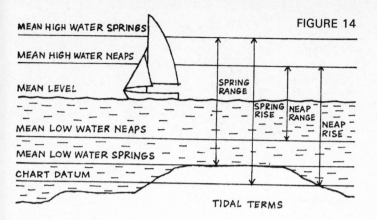

FIGURE 14

MEAN HIGH WATER SPRINGS

MEAN HIGH WATER NEAPS

MEAN LEVEL

SPRING RANGE

SPRING RISE

NEAP RANGE

MEAN LOW WATER NEAPS

NEAP RISE

MEAN LOW WATER SPRINGS

CHART DATUM

TIDAL TERMS

Tidal Streams

Tides do not flow in and out evenly. The tides are affected by the geographical configurations of the coast, by the depth of water, and by the narrowness of outlets. Admiralty Tidal Stream Atlases give the direction and rate of tidal streams, and these must be allowed for, and if possible used.

For example: A small boat under sail will proceed at something between 4 and 6 knots. Against a 3 kt. tide, little progress will be made but *with it* your speed could increase by up to 75%! Wind against tide conditions can lead to a very nasty sea, and no place for a small boat. This, too, must be taken into consideration.

Tidal Stream Table

Charts have Tidal stream information. If for example you examine your chart you will find on it a series of diamonds in purple, each with a letter Ⓑ. On the top of the chart you will find a table and under Ⓑ you will find a table giving the Time, Rate (Springs and Neaps) and direction of tides at that point on the chart.

Don't forget to refer to it, and use the information in your calculation.

Twelfth's Rule

The tide ebbs and flows for about six hours each way, but not at a constant rate. It flows most strongly in the middle two hours and then slows before slack water, then slowly ebbs to ebb strongly again in the 3rd and 4th hour. This has given rise to what is known as the 12th's Rule, which deals with height, not speed.

1st hour after H.W. or before L.W. —
$$\text{difference} = 1/12\text{th of predicted tide}$$

2nd hour after H.W. or before L.W. —
$$\text{difference} = 2/12\text{ths of predicted tide}$$

3rd hour after H.W. or before L.W. —
$$\text{difference} = 3/12\text{ths of predicted tide}$$

4th hour after H.W. or before L.W. —
$$\text{difference} = 3/12\text{ths of predicted tide}$$

5th hour after H.W. or before L.W. —
$$\text{difference} = 2/12\text{ths of predicted tide}$$

6th hour after H.W. or before L.W. —
$$\text{difference} = 1/12\text{th of predicted tide}$$

So Tidal Range = 12ft.

1st hour —	1ft.
2nd hour —	2ft.
3rd hour —	3ft.

Total rise after 3 hours = 6ft.

Reading a Tide Table

You will find tide tables in Reeds and most of the yachting magazines. They give the tides for weeks, months or the year ahead, and together with a tidal flow chart and some local knowledge give you the information necessary to calculate when you can leave port, or cross a shallow. A typical section of a tide table looks like this:-

MAY		HIGH WATER AT DOVER	
	Time	M	Feet
1	0200	0.6	1.7
Wed	0815	7.5	22.5
	1430	0.7	1.8
	2200	7.6	23.0

0815 is HIGH WATER
0200 is LOW WATER

Notice the extreme range of the tide — we are getting near 'Springs'. If the difference between High and Low was much smaller, we would be in or near 'Neaps'.

Working the Tides

The small boat sailor must work the tides. You must try and go with them whenever possible, planning your voyage to take advantage of their assistance, and plotting your course to avoid their most adverse effects. Much of this will come with experience, but always take tidal information into your calculations and the experience on using them will develop.

6

Buoyage and Shore Markers

Though all buoys have a very definite and distinct meaning, there is really very little need to make a fetish of learning them. The I.A.L.A. system now being introduced will cause more trouble to experts than it will to the beginner, for the latter has nothing to unlearn.

Buoys

Buoys are used to mark navigable channels and various kinds of dangers. They are placed in the interests of commercial shipping and this gives the first clue. A rock covered by at least 2 fathoms of water at low tide is a major hazard to almost all ships. To the small boat sailor its only importance is that it may cause breaking waves in bad weather. So, having checked the rock *and its depth* on the chart we may, if we wish, ignore the marking buoys completely in fair conditions.

In buoyed waters used by commercial shipping, small boats are usually safer if they stay *out* of the channel, unless the water outside is excessively shallow, has steep sandbanks, or other hazards. Again, the chart will show you whether you may safely navigate outside the channel or not, and usually you can. A careful study of the chart, along your plotted course, will reveal these features and possible hazards.

Some buoys can be ignored, and some should be positively disobeyed—in each case with due reference to the chart. Even those which you *must* watch, for example those showing the way into a drying harbour at about half tide, will be clearly marked on the chart. The chart and the 5011 will also show you the shape and colour, together with any identifying marks, and day-cruising using chart and 5011 will soon teach you about them.

This is NOT to say ignore the subject completely at this stage. It may fall to your lot to enter a strange harbour without a proper chart, or there will be some hazard newly formed, like the multiple wrecks in the English Channel a few years ago. For these reasons it is essential to understand buoyage, but as your early cruising, chart reading and navigation attempts will either be as crew, or in familiar waters, you can afford to take time to learn this part very gently, by practice, but you must not neglect the opportunity to learn while you have the chance.

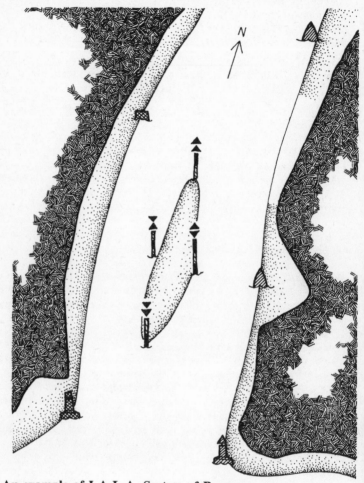

An example of I.A.L.A. System of Buoyage.

FIGURE 15

 RED   YELLOW   GREEN

I.A.L.A. System

The main features of the standard European system are shown in Fig. 15. Channel marking buoys, port hand to left, red, flat topped, starboard hand to right, green, conical, are used to show the best way *into* a port, or *up* a river. Note carefully the *into* and *up*. It is supposed that a ship entering a harbour will be in greater need of assistance than one leaving, so the buoys are all right-way-round when entering. On leaving port, of course, they appear on the opposite side.

Cardinal System

Dangers are marked by *cardinal* buoys, the important feature of which is the 'topmark', consisting of triangles, points up or down to show the direction of the danger. The illustration (Fig. 15) shows which is which.

Buoys do have one great use for the small boat sailor, however. They are all identified by names or numbers both on the chart and on the buoys. Hence they establish an accurate position. It is, therefore, very convenient indeed, in making a passage, to sail up close to a buoy, identify it, and know exactly where you are. You can then set a course for another buoy which is more or less in the right direction, find and identify that one, and so on. I once came into Milford Haven in thick fog by this process. The buoys there are only about ½ to ¾ miles apart, and with great care, using chart and compass, we found and identified each one in turn, never seeing the shore until right by the Fish Dock entrance.

Even in clear weather, the process is very useful. It is well worth planning a trip to pass close by as many buoys as possible, even though it may not be the most direct line to your destination. Each time you arrive at one identified buoy, you know exactly where you are, and this will give you great peace of mind. Never assume, though, that because a buoy is in the right position, it's the right buoy. Go and check — using those binoculars!

In some cases there still are buoys to mark channels in the open sea, though they are now changing. Convention says that the 'handing' is such as to be correct when going in the same direction as the flood tide.

'Unofficial' Buoys

A word of warning here concerning buoys which are not the official Trinity House ones but buoys laid by other authorities. Such buoys may be useful, and they may be marked on the chart. Where they are marked they are likely to be in the right place. But, if the

SPIRE
(Conspic)

BEACON

FIGURE 16

R.A.F. for example, want to move a target buoy, or take it away, or lay an extra one, this is not necessarily covered by 'Notices to Mariners' and may not appear on even a fully corrected chart. Use such buoys as a bonus, but do not rely on them. The colours and patterns are always such as not to be confused with any genuine navigational buoy.

Some marks ashore are maintained by Trinity House, and these are always marked on charts. The best known are lighthouses, which are rarely close enough to one another to cause any confusion. The Admiralty 'Pilots'. quite often give illustrations, especially if there is any possible doubt.

Leading Marks
'Leading Marks' are another type of shore marker. They consist of 2 posts, or pylons, usually carrying lights for night use, which must be kept in line to ensure that you are in a certain channel, or clear of certain rocks. The lower mark is always the seaward one, nearest to you, so the interpretation will be as shown in Fig. 16.

'Measured distances' use 2 pairs of posts, start and finish being as the posts come in line to your side. All such things are shown on the chart. Just as with buoys, other objects ashore may be shown, and used as navigational marks, but they are always less trustworthy than genuine navigational marks.

*   *   *   *

Summary
We have now purchased, installed and checked our compass, prepared our charts and learned to read them with a 5011; we understand buoyage and have some idea of the effects of tides, and should be ready to try out our new equipment and theoretical knowledge on a short day-cruise.

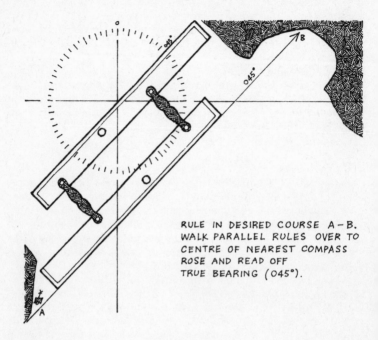

RULE IN DESIRED COURSE A – B.
WALK PARALLEL RULES OVER TO
CENTRE OF NEAREST COMPASS
ROSE AND READ OFF
TRUE BEARING (045°).

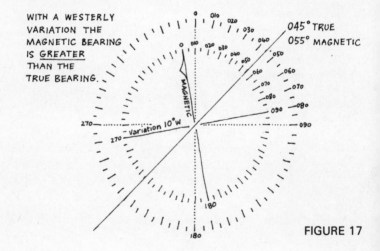

WITH A WESTERLY
VARIATION THE
MAGNETIC BEARING
IS GREATER
THAN THE
TRUE BEARING.

045° TRUE
055° MAGNETIC

FIGURE 17

7

Shaping a Course and Fixes

PLOTTING A COURSE means finding out where you've been. Shaping a course means working out where you want to go.

Most people seem to regard shaping and plotting a course as the height of cruising skill. In my opinion, the most important rule is KNOW WHERE YOU ARE.

First Steps

SHAPING a course means deciding in which direction to point the boat, and which heading or headings to set on the compass to arrive at your destination.

Apart from establishing the chart course, converting it to magnetic and compass bearings, allowances must be made, as we have already seen, for the effect of tides, tidal streams, leeway and deviation. Not to mention wind and weather!

On top of all this, most navigators develop a sort of HUNCH, which says add or subtract a degree or two. If you ask them, they can't say why, but they are usually right!

The mechanics of plotting a course are usually easy, but in a small boat like a dinghy, the speed is so variable that truly accurate prediction is impossible. What you must do is make an intelligent calculation, and include such features as:

Calculated Speed
Wind force and direction
Tidal speed and direction
Deviation

and so on ... and so on ... and so on ...

Shaping a Course

The steps are as follows:

1. Firstly, study tide tables and flow charts to determine if at the desired time you have enough water to leave port, and that the tides are not foul.

2. Then rule in the desired course on the chart. Walk the rule over to the compass rose, the rule running through the centre plot of the 'rose' and read off the true bearing. Study the course—does it run you aground, into any shallows, across a

43

tide race—can you *make* that course good? If not, you may have to plot a course with several 'legs'. Let us assume that you can make it, for even if you have to sail it on several 'legs', the procedure for each 'leg' will be the same.

Shaping Procedure

Let us be quite clear about what we are trying to do. We are trying on land to plot a course that will, in a small boat, take us from point A to point B. Consulting your chart, almanac and tidal flow charts you will get the basic information.

Chart course (say)	090°T
Variation (off chart)	
8°W	+8°
so magnetic course	=098°M
Deviation on this heading	
+3°	= +3°
	101°C

So our compass course would be 101°C.

Note: T = True (off chart).
M = Magnetic (with variation).
C = Compass (with deviation).

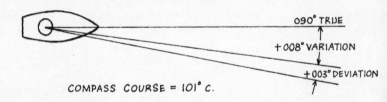

COMPASS COURSE = 101° C.

FIGURE 18

However, there are three other factors: tidal set, and leeway, and your speed. The effect of the tidal stream will affect the heading. Let us assume that the tide is heading 180° at 2 kts. and the boat is making 5 kts. through the water. In other words for every 5 kts. forward she is being carried 2 sea miles south. You can get this information off the tidal flow charts plus a little 'hunch'.

Now you can do a simple calculation, from the following information.

Your direct course is from A to B = 090°T.

Your variation is 8°W.

Your deviation on this heading is 3°.

Your tidal set South at 2 kts.

Your speed (estimated) is 5 kts.

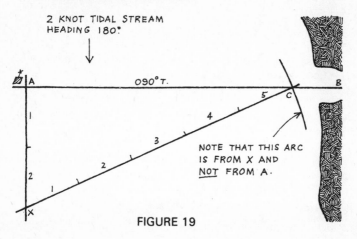

FIGURE 19

So, from A, and using the latitude second scale off the side of the chart at a point level with your position, lay off a point 2 sea miles south of the line AB. This allows for the tidal drift.

Next, adjust the dividers for a speed of 5 kts. (your estimated speed) and from X describe an arc cutting the line AB at point C.

Now with the rule, draw in a line XC and walk this line over to the compass rose, to get another true bearing—which will be 067°T.

This tells us how much, and where, we will be carried in one hour and what course alteration is necessary to counteract it.

Without existing information we can now do the following calculation:

True course	=	067°T
Variation	=	+8°
Mag. course	=	075°M

45

The deviation on this heading, however, is +5°.

075°M

Plus deviation   +5°

Compass course   =   080°C

This is the course that you would set on your compass. There is, however, one final calculation: Leeway.

Leeway

All sailing craft make some leeway. Just how much depends on their build, their point of sailing, and the way they are handled. The action of the wind pushes the boat sideways, and the keel or centreboard's main job is to counteract this sideways motion.

The course the boat is making will be revealed by the wake. Take a bearing from the fore-and-aft line of the boat, over the stern, and compare this with the curve of the wake.

In the example below the heading (090°C) must be adjusted 10° from 090°C to 080°C. Always adjust *INTO* the wind.

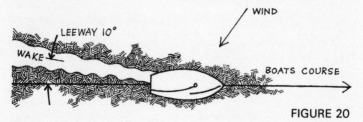

FIGURE 20

Fixes

This will set you off in the right direction (you hope) but you can't leave it there. The wind may change, the tidal flow will slacken, and errors will occur in your helming. You must be continually monitoring your progress.

The basic calculation of a simple fix — which means to fix or find your position — uses an angle and a distance. For example, I may be 2 miles Southwest of Dungeness Lighthouse. There is a definite distance from one fixed reference point, and at a definite angle, 45°, from the N-S reference line (line of longitude) which passes through Dungeness Lighthouse. If you can see it, it's possibly all too obvious. Never forget, though, that it takes *two* measurements of some kind to fix a position, and each measurement must refer to well defined basics. The best

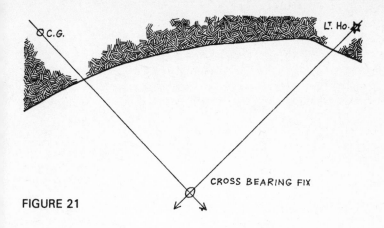

C.G.

Lᵀ. Ho.

CROSS BEARING FIX

FIGURE 21

measurement is two angles, (see the sketch of an imaginary piece of coastline Fig. 21). Here, measuring the angles and (after converting to True) drawing them on the chart will fix your position.

You will doubtless realise that the lighthouse and C.G. station are fixed, but remember you have also made use of a fixed N.S. axis. Don't forget variation if you measure these angles with a magnetic compass!

Whether you realise it or not, you've plotted a 'fix'. In this case, by bearing on the lighthouse, you have established one 'position line'. You are *somewhere* along that line, but, except by guesswork, you have no means of knowing how far. By means of a second 'position line' which crosses the first, you establish the missing distance, since there is only *one* point which is on *both* lines. It's even better if you have *three* position lines.

There are ways of establishing the distance along a single line but they involve the use of either a sextant or a rangefinder. By the time you have progressed to these instruments, I hope you have appreciated their uses, or be reading a much more advanced book than this one.

'Fixes' may rely on 2 lines crossing, and for accuracy, the more nearly at right angles they are, the better. Always try to get a third line if possible, and even though you will very rarely indeed get a perfect 3-line cross, the triangle or 'cocked hat' should be reasonably small (Fig. 24). If one line is wildly awry from the other two, then there is an error somewhere. I have, of course, used the

47

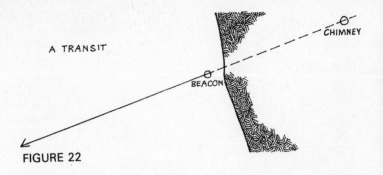

A TRANSIT

CHIMNEY

BEACON

FIGURE 22

easy, classic way to describe fixes, but in practice, position lines may be derived in all kinds of ways. You are trying to find out where you are, that's all. A few examples are given here, and the experienced navigator will, at times, use all of them, and probably even more, for the great rule in Navigation is: *Always know where you are.* So look out for, or use:

1. Hand bearing compass, as already explained.
2. Two marks ashore exactly in line, (or a TRANSIT). (Fig. 22)
3. Variants of this, say 2 headlands exactly in line, or the length of a pier in line.
4. A shore mark *exactly* abeam of the boat, by sighting along some feature definitely known to be at right angles to your fore and aft line, e.g. thwart or transom. (Fig. 23)
5. A well defined submarine contour i.e. changes in depth — note, position lines do not have to be straight.
6. Being *exactly* between 2 marks — possibly buoys. It needs care to know if the bearings ahead and astern are exactly opposite, but it can be done.
7. On an arc of a circle if you *know* you have travelled an exact distance from a fixed mark, but are not sure of direction.
8. By reference to a fixed known course of a regular ferry steamer.

These methods are getting less reliable as we go down the list, but any information is useful, and the whole process becomes an attitude of mind, gathering *all sorts of bits and pieces to make a composite picture.* Most of the basic information is already on the chart. You just have to practice using it.

This is theory. At sea you may well find that all of the sources of information do not agree with one another, and you will have to

48

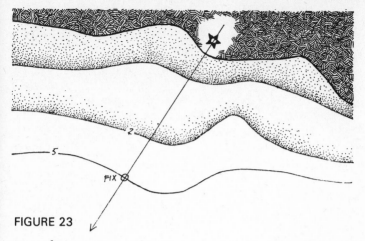

FIGURE 23

assess why, or compromise. You must be able to re-check your sources. Use those which are reliable, and always prefer genuine marine markers or physical features ashore.

Now, since it is very important, let us revise and then practise these fixes.

Simple Fix (Fig. 21).
An accurate fix can be obtained when you can take a bearing (a magnetic bearing) on *two or more* objects ashore and plot these bearings (converted to True) on your chart.

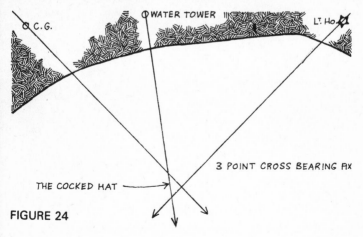

3 POINT CROSS BEARING FIX

THE COCKED HAT ⟶

FIGURE 24

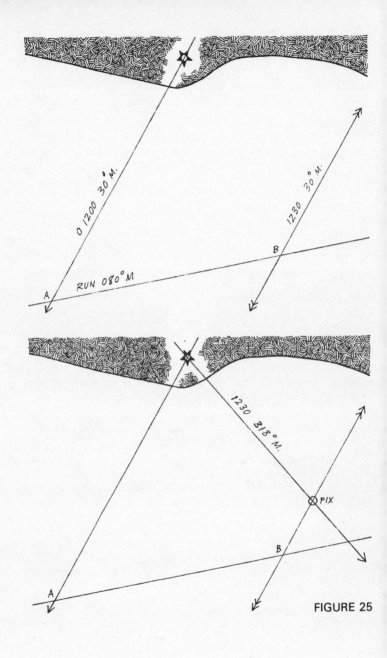

FIGURE 25

The "Cocked Hat" (Fig. 24).

If you can take a bearing on three objects and draw in the lines you may get a triangle on the chart, which is known as a 'cocked hat'. You will be somewhere inside it. Assume you are at the least favourable point.

Running Fix

Remember you need two items for a fix. In this case, where you have only *one* object to take a bearing on, you take *two* bearings of it at a timed interval.

In this example, you take a bearing on the lighthouse at 1200 hours. It bears 030°M. Draw this on the chart. This is your *first position line*. Your course is 080°M and at *any* point (A) on the first position line, draw in your course.

Your speed is 4 kts. and at 1230 when you have covered 2 sea miles, you mark a point (B) on your course line, and with the parallel rule draw in a line parallel to the first position line and cutting B. This is the *transferred position line*. You take another bearing on the lighthouse and draw this on the chart. This is your *second position line*, and bears 318°M.

Draw in the bearing 318M (the second position line) and where this cuts the transferred position line—you are. (Fig. 25).

This is a simple example, and if there is much tidal set this too must be included in your calculations.

Dead Reckoning

The whole basis of dead reckoning is that you have a definite point to start from, such as your point of departure or last definite fix. A dead reckoning position is a calculated guess or estimate, and needs to be recorded as such on the chart, until you can 'fix' your position.

You must establish a 'deck log' which is a record, with *exact times* of each change of course, any fixed objects passed, and of the best possible estimates of distance and/or speed. From this, at the end of each hour, all this information and timings are plotted on the chart, so that you know not what you *hoped* to achieve, but what you *have* achieved. This process is called 'Dead Reckoning', and is the basic navigation process used by 90% of small boats. It is as accurate as your care can make it, and can be surprisingly good, to within a couple of miles after a Channel crossing of up to 80 miles or so. The example as shown in Fig. 26 will give you a general idea.

51

You can also learn and use the other methods like doubling the angle on the box, fixing by bearings and transits referring to the sighted distance of known objects, like lighthouses or by sounding. Whatever you do, remember—*ALWAYS KNOW WHERE YOU ARE.*

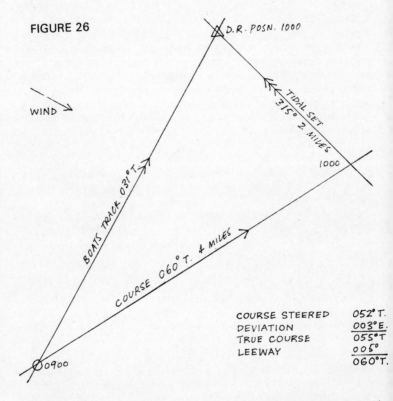

FIGURE 26

WIND

BOATS TRACK 031° T.

TIDAL SET 315° 2 MILES

D.R. POSN. 1000

1000

COURSE 060° T. 4 MILES

0900

COURSE STEERED	052° T.
DEVIATION	003° E.
TRUE COURSE	055° T
LEEWAY	005°
	060° T.

Note: The *DR position* is: Boat's corrected heading plus logged distance.

Estimated position is: Boat's plus heading plus logged distance plus tide plus leeway.

8
Planning a Cruise

So, you have your boat, the best compass you can afford, the charts of the area you want to sail in and a crew willing to join you in an expedition along the coast. How do you go about organizing it? The prime object is to get to your destination safely and with as little upset as possible, and to do this *preparation* must be the key word.

Certain facts must be taken for granted, or carefully checked: that you can sail competently; that your boat is seaworthy; the forecast is good, and tides favourable; that you have the necessary ancillary equipment such as anchor, oars, bucket, spare clothing, food and, of course, flares, to name just a few.

Right! What do you want to do? Are you going on from your first destination to another, or is it to be a day expedition out and back to your start point? Let us take just the simple day expedition of say 6 to 8 miles to a destination and then returning to the launching place.

Pre-planning (Fig. 27).
The initial planning can and should be done well in advance and, in fact, many cold winter evenings may be spent pleasantly thinking and planning your summer trips. The first consideration will be the actual route you will want to cover. You should make notes of the following:

1. Are there any hazards such as sandbanks, rough water areas, or even old wrecks? What prominent landmarks, lighthouses or buoys are you going to pass? Make a list of them, in the order that they will appear, so that when you are out there you will know what to look for, and what should come next.

2. What distance are you going to cover? Join your start point and your destination with a ruled line on the chart and look at the chart to seek hidden dangers, shallows and harbour bars. Also measure the distance using the latitude scale off the side of the chart as this will give you a clue as to how long it will, or should, take you. Most small boats will average around 3 to 4 knots (nautical miles per hour) in moderate conditions, and with experience you will know the speed of your particular boat in various wind strengths and different points of sailing. Remember that time = distance divided by speed.

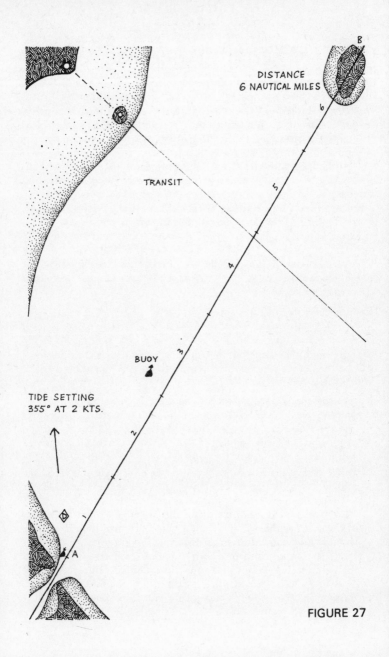

DISTANCE
6 NAUTICAL MILES

TRANSIT

BUOY

TIDE SETTING
355° AT 2 KTS.

FIGURE 27

Tide Direction and Speed—Tide Tables

You will need to know the time of high water on the day in question, so that you can launch or leave harbour and so that you can use the tidal stream to best advantage. It is silly to spend several hours sailing against a tidal current when, leaving earlier or later, you can have the tide with you. Of course, you might not want to get up early in the morning to catch the tide, but that is your decision. In which case it might be better to go the following weekend when the tide may be more favourable.

So, now we have a *day* on which to sail, a *distance* we wish to sail, a *destination* and the *time of high water*. Looking at the chart, you will see some diamonds with letters in them, like this ◈, and at the bottom or top of the chart a box full of numbers. The letter in the diamond refers to a column in the tidal flow box. Use the one nearest to your course.

Plotting the Tide

To plot the tide direction, the bearing (355°) is taken *either* from the compass rose (remember it is a true bearing) and transferred to the start point by use of parallel rules (Fig. 28) or, for small boat work especially, a 'Douglas Protractor' is used to plot the bearing (Fig. 29).

Having plotted the *bearing* it is necessary to plot the *rate*. In this example, the rate is 2 kts and therefore the tide in one hour will move the boat a *distance* of 2 sea-miles along the *bearing* 259°. If a large scale chart is being used, any unit of scale to reduce this size of the tidal plot will suffice. Remember what scale unit you use, because it is going to be needed again. You can use any scale, but it must, for any series of calculations, *always be the same one*. Use the dividers, mark off the distance the tide will take you *from* the start point *along* the bearing (Fig. 30).

Speed

The next consideration is the boat's speed. It is very difficult in a small boat to know exactly how fast you are moving. Even with instruments to help it is difficult. However, any large error that is put into the calculation at this stage will show up fairly quickly if you have studied your route carefully and know what buoys, or marks, should be coming up. Once under way, you will want to take a 'fix' after 20 minutes or so to get an update on where you are and this again will show up any error. Let us say that we reckon the boat will average 4 knots. From the point where the tide plot finished (X) using the dividers opened to

FIGURE 28

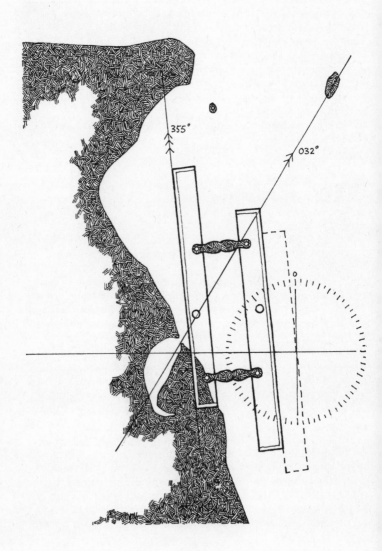

355°

032°

FIGURE 29

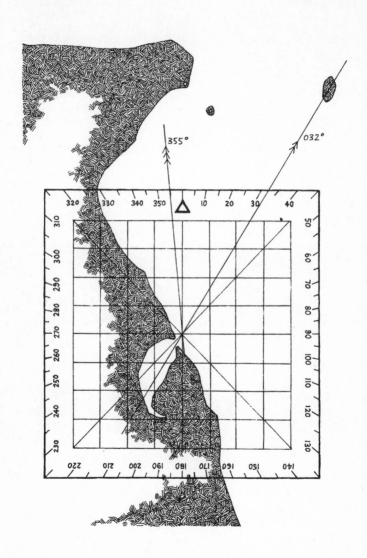

4 miles (using that same unit scale) mark back to the course line (Fig. 30). Now join the two points together. The bearing we must sail on is the bearing of line X-C. The distance we will travel in the first hour is A-C. Remember that unit scale, 6 miles (speed of boat + tide).

Converting Bearings
This bearing is in degrees True and will need to be converted to magnetic. In a small boat deviation is difficult to assess, and if the compass has been installed as we have described, with the aim of eliminating errors, deviation may perhaps be ignored. It would be worth checking the steering compass with a hand-bearing compass to see how different they are, if you suspect that large errors exist.

Leeway
The final problem will be leeway, the amount of sideway drift which is always present, but varies according to the point of sailing and the type of boat. This can be calculated after the trip has commenced, but remember always to allow for any leeway by turning the boat a little more, maybe 3-5° towards the wind. With experience, you will know the amount of leeway to allow for each point of sailing and wind strength.

Even while sitting at home the next hour's sailing could be calculated from the chart and tables until you complete the passage. The problem is that this may be good practice in 'armchair navigation', but in the real situation the planning all goes by the board when that first fix is taken and you find yourself off course! Then everything has to change to meet the new situation; a new start point has been found, and the whole process has to be repeated, using updated information, to either get you back on to your original course, or to give you a new compass course to reach your destination. For instance, there may be another tidal diamond nearer to your new start point. The time factor will have changed. Your boat's speed will now be more accurate. The new course you come up with will need a new estimation of leeway.

So there it is. There are four steps in pre-planning:

Plan it as best as you can.

Sail it for a while.

Check where you are with a fix.

Re-plan with the updated information.

58

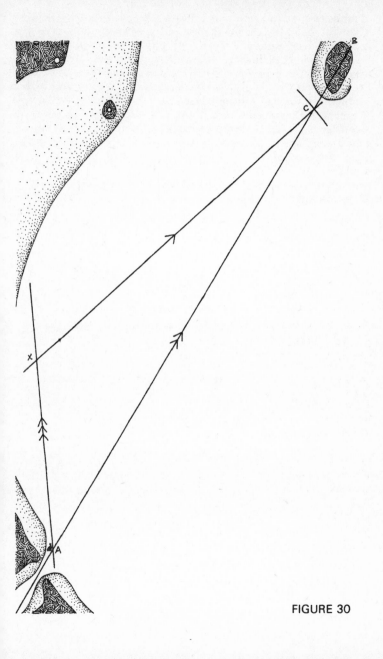

FIGURE 30

Transits

For the small boat sailor the use of transits is probably the most accurate and easiest way of crossing the tidal stream. To sail a transit you must line up two objects, and then keep the boat sailing a course so that the objects stay in line. This must mean that you have to point the boat into the tidal stream. But by how much will depend on the boat's speed and the rate of the tidal stream. If the two objects do not stay in line, and they rarely do for any length of time, turn the boat towards the nearer of the two and they will eventually line up again. If you have the ability to sail transits they can be taken into consideration when planning the course, and transits noted on the chart. One point worth a mention is that the actual transit line should be on the course you *wish* to sail.

Check and Re-Check

As you can see there are many factors which go into the process of converting a bearing, plotting a course on the chart, and converting all this into the bearing you set on the compass. Even when you think you have done the job successfully, do NOT believe it! You must check and re-check. You must keep a 'dead reckoning' plot going, and be prepared to alter your course forecast at any time. Indeed, you must *expect* to alter it, as the voyage progresses.

9
The Weather

No work on small craft navigation would be complete without some reference to the weather. The wind dominates small boat sailing; whatever plans you may have in mind, or whatever course you have plotted, will have to be completely re-calculated if the weather turns nasty.

As a basic rule, *Over Force-4—forget it!* And if you *do* go, get good weather information before you leave.

Weather Forecasts
The yachtsman is well provided with forecasts, both on T.V. and radio and in the national press. Radio forecasts are the most frequent, up-to-date, and readily available, and, although the broadcast times are constantly changed, they are given in the local paper or the Radio Times and you should listen to them. The shipping forecast, and Coastal reports, are a must for all small boat sailors.

There are weather stations all round the coast, and you can ring them up for a forecast.

None of the information they give you will be much help if you don't know what it means.

The Spur Venture Guide, *Weather Lore*, will give you a good grasp of the subject.

Wind Against Tide
Wind against tide can kick up a very nasty sea. If your plotted course is not with the tide and before, say, the prevailing westerly wind, remember that, should the wind freshen, you may have a hard beat back in the evening.

You might well plot a return course through the most sheltered water available.

The Beaufort Scale
Study this chart. It gives the information on sea and land indications of wind force, and you will find it essential.

BEAUFORT WIND SCALE

Beaufort Number	Limits of Wind Speed in Knots	Descriptive Terms	Sea Criterion	Land Conditions
0	Less than 1	Calm	Like a mirror.	Smoke rises vertically.
1	1–3	Light air	Ripples but without foam crests.	Flags flap slightly.
2	4–6	Light breeze	Small wavelets with unbroken crests.	Leaves rustle; wind felt on face.
3	7–10	Gentle breeze	Large wavelets, with perhaps scattered white horses.	Leaves in motion; flags flap.
4	11–16	Moderate breeze	Small waves; frequent white horses.	Dust rises; branches sway.
5	17–21	Fresh breeze	Moderate waves, more pronounced; many white horses; perhaps some spray.	Small trees sway.
6	22–27	Strong breeze	Large waves forming; extensive white foam crests; likelihood of spray.	Telephone lines whistle; umbrellas hard to hold.
7	28–33	Near gale	Sea heaps up with white foam blown in streaks along direction of wind.	Trees sway; hard to walk.
8	34–40	Gale	Moderately high waves; foam blown in definite streaks along direction of wind.	Twigs fall; cars buffeted.
9	41–47	Strong gale	High waves; crests tumble and roll.	Twigs fall; cars buffeted.
10	48–55	Storm	Very high waves; heavy tumbling waves; poor visibility.	Trees fall.
11	56–63	Violent storm	Exceptionally high waves. Sea completely covered with long white foam lying along direction of wind. Wave crests blown into froth. Poor visibility.	
12	64+	Hurricane	Air filled with foam and spray. Very poor visibility.	

10
A Little Knowledge

The navigator who knows everything about the subject has not yet been born, nor is he ever likely to be. Those people who *think* they know all about it should contribute very heavily toward the Royal National Lifeboat Institution, whose services they will certainly need before long.

In this book I have tried to emphasise the care and accuracy needed with the two fundamentals, Chart and Compass. We have looked at various other instruments, books and sources of information, and some basic navigational theory. This will get you started, and if you exercise caution you will soon get the feel of it.

Pilotage
A deep-sea man does not call this navigation in the true sense. When he thinks of 'navigation' he thinks of star sights and sextants, and great circle courses. This coastal work we have covered here, into and out of ports, along rivers, and across estuaries, is more properly called Pilotage. It calls for a great amount of local knowledge, and is justifiably said to be as much an art as a science.

Sea-going commercial ships 'take a Pilot' to enter harbour. As amateurs, we do not, but we must know much of what the pilot knows. We do not usually need to worry too much over the depth of water, and our boat is much more manoeuvrable, which makes the job a little easier, but currents affect us just as much or more than they do a large ship.

Local Knowledge
Make friends with fishermen, lifeboat crews and coastguards wherever you voyage. Their intimate knowledge of local conditions is yours for the asking. Be ignorant; ask *why* does such a peculiar eddy occur, *why* are tides irregular, *why* does a certain wind kick up a horrible sea? And then *listen*, don't argue. You will learn better and remember more than any book can possibly explain.

Equally, you must try and keep out of trouble because these people, together with the Coastguard, may have the job of getting you out of it.

Training Courses

Knowledge, experience and caution are the fundamental skills. You can learn the first and develop the others, but good instruction helps.

Further training and more advanced navigation can be learnt at evening classes, by reading or by attending courses etc ... the National Sailing Centre, Arctic Road, Cowes, Isle of Wight, runs some excellent ones.

If this book has whetted your appetite for navigation, why not write for their brochure?

Practice

As you will realise, the good navigator makes continual calculations and as he gains experience, introduces an element of 'hunch' (which sounds better than guesswork). He or she is always on the lookout — always noting little indications to help plot a more accurate fix, or give a better estimate of progress.

Continual practice will not only help develop your 'hunch', but eradicate the errors that you will undoubtedly make to begin with.

You will forget the variation, or put it the wrong way. You will forget leeway, or make a hash of your tides, or the helm may not be able to lay the course you want — the possibilities for errors are endless.

Use your common-sense. If a calculation just doesn't make sense, do it again.

A navigational error can have serious consequences for craft and crew. This book is only designed to teach a complete beginner the absolute basics. It is, however, quite adequate to get you going on short cruises and day trips. So go and practise, never stop learning, and good luck to you in all your ventures.